THROUGH
THEIR EYES

UK VERSES

Edited By Wendy Laws

First published in Great Britain in 2020 by:

Young Writers
Remus House
Coltsfoot Drive
Peterborough
PE2 9BF
Telephone: 01733 890066
Website: www.youngwriters.co.uk

Printed and bound in the UK by BookPrintingUK
Website: www.bookprintinguk.com
YB0433V

FOREWORD

Since 1991, here at Young Writers we have celebrated the awesome power of creative writing, especially in young adults, where it can serve as a vital method of expressing strong (and sometimes difficult) emotions, a conduit to develop empathy, and a safe, non-judgemental place to explore one's own place in the world. With every poem we see the effort and thought that each pupil published in this book has put into their work and by creating this anthology we hope to encourage them further with the ultimate goal of sparking a life-long love of writing.

Through Their Eyes challenged young writers to open their minds and pen bold, powerful poems from the points-of-view of any person or concept they could imagine – from celebrities and politicians to animals and inanimate objects, or even just to give us a glimpse of the world as they experience it. The result is this fierce collection of poetry that by turns questions injustice, imagines the innermost thoughts of influential figures or simply has fun.

The nature of the topic means that contentious or controversial figures may have been chosen as the narrators, and as such some poems may contain views or thoughts that, although may represent those of the person being written about, by no means reflect the opinions or feelings of either the author or us here at Young Writers.

We encourage young writers to express themselves and address subjects that matter to them, which sometimes means writing about sensitive or difficult topics. If you have been affected by any issues raised in this book, details on where to find help can be found at *www.youngwriters.co.uk/info/other/contact-lines*

CONTENTS

Millie Grace Finan (11)	76
Alina Jiang (12)	77
Samuel Bowers	78
Hanna Emilia Balcarek (13)	79
Hollie Nugent (12)	80
Imogen Rose Evans (11)	81
Zakir Ali (12)	82
Michael Charnley (11)	83
Abdul-Sami Shakeel	84
Aimee Lee Boileau (11)	85
Meka Faith Reynolds (12)	86
Samuel Stephen Shaw (12)	87
Ikhlaas Goraya (12)	88
Chloe Chirozva	89
Gabrielle Sandra Owen-Davies (11)	90
Iman Ayub	91
Joseph Oluwasola Ogunbo (12)	92
Hasan Amar	93
Talbiya Khandaker	94
Austin Heneghan (11)	95
Arooj Rafiq (12)	96
Adam Garner	97
Adam Najeeb (12)	98
Daniel Parry (12)	99
Sophia Megan Ellison (12)	100
Ali Rehman (12)	101
Zara Hussain (12)	102
Jennifer Rose Harrison (13)	103
Ahmad Hussain (12)	104
Maryam Hussain (12)	105
Imaan Faisal (12)	106
Max Lees (11)	107
Mia Lucy Wilson (13)	108
Samuel Townson (11)	109
Aadam Sattar (11)	110

St Philip Howard Catholic High School, Barnham

Abigail Louise Guppy (12)	111
Isabella Cyrulik (12)	112

Uddingston Grammar School, Uddingston

Sophie Ryder	113

Wallace High School, Stirling

Millie Caplan Johnston (11)	114
Hannah Stretch	116
Keigan Thomas McLaren Robertson (13)	118

Woking High School, Horsell

Chloe Isabella Barwick (11)	119
Jessica Chan (13)	120
Amy Rolfe (13)	122

THE
POEMS

The Priceless Price

I bargained with the White Witch, willing to pay the price,
One where I would be able to restart,
Even though I knew it was a big sacrifice.

But I was not only being nice,
I was also being very smart,
That I bargained with the White Witch, willing to pay the price.

Little did she know the wonders behind the door of life,
So instead she decided to take my precious parts
And that was a painful sacrifice.

Deep down I knew what I was doing was wise,
I knew that I would never have to depart,
Which is why I bargained with the White Witch, willing to make the price.

I always knew she would never think twice,
Before she decided to take my heart,
That it was no longer that much of a sacrifice.

So when I arose from the dead to be precise,
I bellowed with all I had, I feared I would fall apart,
That I bargained with the White Witch, willing to pay the price
Which now does not seem like a big sacrifice.

Shannel Sarpong (12)
Fairfield High School For Girls, Droylsden

Henry VIII And His Six Wives

I am King Henry
Broad and wide
And I was looking for a fair lady
To call my beautiful bride.

The first up was Catherine,
A horrid wife she was,
Of course, I never really liked her
And the reason for this is because...

I wanted a child, a boy you see,
I wanted one with all my heart,
But Catherine couldn't give me one of those,
So I told her we had to part.

It's rather sad, you see, for me of course,
My life was unbearably bad,
But it was my second wife, however,
That made me even more mad.

I cannot begin to describe to you
All the things she did and said,
But let's just say, I felt the need,
To separate Anne Boleyn from her head.

Next up was Jane Seymour,
How it hurts to say the name,
I asked for a baby boy, my dear,
Not for all this pain.

I miss her so much, and even more so,
Because she gave me my bundle of joy,
Oh well, on with my life,
At least now I have my baby boy.

Anne of Cleves, oh how it makes me wince,
Every time I say her name,
If only when I met her she looked like what
Was inside that picture frame.

Really though, can you blame me,
For already picking out my next wife?
As a middle-aged man, I felt I needed by now
At least some form of a life.

I thought Catherine Howard was the one
But as I discovered a bit more about her past,
Being the smart person I am I realised
We really weren't going to last.

Last up is Catherine Parr,
We were wed until I tragically died,
But lucky for her she got the crown of
'Henry the Eighth's final bride'.

So there you go, that is how
We all came to the end of our lives,
Now you know nearly everything
About me and my six wives.

Katy Lauren Hemsworth (12)
Fairfield High School For Girls, Droylsden

The Universe

Let me tell you a story,
The story is about a long dream.

I scattered the atoms of a person in the grass, the air, the
sea and the rivers.
A woman gathered them; she drank, ate, inhaled them.
The woman assembled this person in her body.
The person awoke from the warm, dark, safe world of its
mother
And was dropped into this long dream.
The person was a new story, written in letters of DNA.
A new program, a new being.
This person, this person was only a speck compared to what
I have made, but I loved it anyway.
It didn't know I existed, but neither does anything else on
Earth.
I still had my ways of telling it that I loved it.
Through the twinkle of a star, or through the falling leaf
from a tree.
In those moments, I knew it felt love because that was me
loving it.
As time went on, and as the Earth orbited the sun, the
person grew.
I scattered more atoms and more women gathered them.
New life, new programs, new beings were all made,
And as I loved every one of them,
I carried on loving the person because my love is the
undying type.

Everything I make comes to an end eventually.
Every star, every planet, every life.
I am the only thing that is here forever.
So as the person closes its eyes for the last time,
It wakes up from its dream and leaps into the stars.
It curls up on the ball of blazing gas and falls asleep.
It waits for me to scatter the atoms,
And when I do, it starts a new dream.
A new life. A new program. A new being.
I am the universe.
You are the new person in this new dream.
It's time to wake up.

Sophia Ledward (12)
Fairfield High School For Girls, Droylsden

David Walliams And His Depression

I was lonely.
It was hard.
No matter how hard I tried to make myself happier,
It didn't work.

I was always so pessimistic,
So hopeless,
I isolated myself,
I was trapped in my negativity.

She became pregnant,
It was hard
And stressful.
The morning sickness,
Making sure everything was perfect,
The room, the cot, the hospital bag,
For when you were ready to come.

The nine months were over in a flash,
He was ready to come
And after hours of questioning
His name was decided,
Little Alfred was now in our lives and care.

For the first time in a million years,
I felt happier than I had ever done,
For little Alfred was born.
Someone I could love and care for every second

For the rest of my life.

Thank you, my dear son, Alfred
For saving me from my loneliest times,
That were all of a sudden
Going to get worse
And I know now
If it wasn't for you
I would never be happy again.

Emily Jayne Price (12)
Fairfield High School For Girls, Droylsden

Nemo

N ever-ending ocean,
so much to explore,
but I'm not allowed to leave the anemone,
my dad is such a bore.

E veryone having independence
but me starting school late,
my dad afraid of me getting lost
with my lucky fin and defenceless state.

M ore curiosity creeping forward
trying to leave at all costs.
Swimming to touch the floating proof of strength
but I was snatched by divers and now I'm lost!

O ceans no more, not a reef to be seen,
only lost fish that also lost their minds.
A yellow fish called Bubbles whose name suggests his
pastime,
with others in a tank we'll stay that's full of grease and
grime.
They say the fish murderer will take me, I fear my dad's too
late.
I wait to hear if this is the end and if it is my fate...

Freyja Stone (12)
Fairfield High School For Girls, Droylsden

Blue Cadillac

Speeding down the highway, in your blue Cadillac,
Top down, I can feel the wind in my hair.
It feels like I'm flying.
I can feel your gaze and feel your smile.
Speeding down the highway in your blue Cadillac,
Top town, I can see the white cliffs and the blue-green
ocean.
It looks like heaven.
I can see the state of your hair and the twinkle in your eye
as I reach for the volume of the radio.
Speeding down the highway in your blue Cadillac,
Top down, I can hear, can hear the song on the radio.
It tells me the story of a girl called Brandy.
I can hear your laugh and your voice telling me to sing
along as the song hits the chorus.
Speeding down the highway in your blue Cadillac,
Top down, loving this car ride with you.

Imaani Steele (12)
Fairfield High School For Girls, Droylsden

Out Of This World

It was a tiny world,
a place too numb and cold,
but her galactic mind
reformed the empty loss of time.

Her need for adventure
and want for a future,
transformed her 'impossible' goals,
into a wandering truth.

She was part of the stars,
a planet of her own,
a portal of opportunity,
a timeless zone.

An aimless bubble
not wanting to pop,
but time took a toll,
in an instant, she dropped

Back down on a gravitated place,
so simplistic and effortlessly tame,
she was the first woman in space,
a place she wanted
to peacefully spend her days,
Valentina Tereshkova.

Zainab Aabru Zaman (13)
Fairfield High School For Girls, Droylsden

Books!

Books help your imagination to grow
Books help you to learn to sew
Sadly I wasn't allowed them though.

They went in the trash
As Father threw them in with an almighty
Crash...

I ran to my room and sobbed
As my books had been robbed.

The pages were in little parts
Like my little broken heart.

The words were all jumbled up
So I could no longer read the book.

So I can only imagine the magic that would happen
If I opened a book.

Frustratingly that was not meant to be
Little sad me, sat on my bed with no book to hand
With only a story in my head,
All for me...

Olivia Jackson (11)
Fairfield High School For Girls, Droylsden

Now You See

Now you see that the world is falling apart,
Now you see that we really are monsters,
Now you see that the children are right,
And the adults are wrong.

Now you know that the world is falling apart,
That everything is not like the start,
That nothing will get better,
It is now or never.

Now we make a difference,
Before we all die,
Before the animals become extinct,
Before plastic is more than fish in the sea,
Before the children have no future,
I can almost see it with my eyes.

Now we see!

Khadija Elkheder (11)
Fairfield High School For Girls, Droylsden

My Mum

I would hold your hand to cross the street at three.
At eight we would go to the park every Saturday.
Soon I left you for my friends,
I didn't want you to drop me off at the gate.
We would argue and I would not talk,
Yet you made me tea and kept it warm.
Now I'm twenty-one and I've got a job,
You taught me everything I needed to know.
You're falling ill and I realise my mistakes.
You are my heart, my moon, my sun, the centre of my universe.
I love you, Mum, for your ever hard work.

Tahira Miah (12)
Fairfield High School For Girls, Droylsden

I Am Emmeline Pankhurst

Running down Moss Side Avenue,
Knowing that everyone knew,
Votes for women shall happen today,
Going forward without delay,
That is my dream anyway.

Really the truth still lies ahead,
There are lots of things I should dread.
Could I be captured and put in a cell,
Or will I be made to live a life of hell!

However, all this might make people give up,
If they come along with me they'll have a full cup.
I am Emmeline Pankhurst and I've not had enough!

Emily Hargreaves (11)
Fairfield High School For Girls, Droylsden

Sir Alex Ferguson

I see, in my eyes,
A successful team,
That play with pride
With a red-devilish theme.

I see, in my eyes,
Many fans and supporters
That follow us to glory
With big banners and posters.

I see, in my eyes,
Many wonderful players,
Midfield, defence, striker,
All the club's layers.

I know, in my heart,
As all our memories unfold,
That this team is a home,
He passes, he shoots and goal!

Elizabeth Stella Pearson (12)
Fairfield High School For Girls, Droylsden

Racing For My Nation

I go up to the edge of the pool,
About to dive and swim
And then I look around me,
Thinking, *will I win?*

When I dive off the block,
I feel a great sensation.
Hoping that one day I will swim for my nation.

Coming up to the end of my race
I needed to keep up the pace.

I was nearly there, just a little further
And then I definitely knew.
My dream of becoming a professional swimmer was actually
going to come true.

Maisie Haslam (11)
Fairfield High School For Girls, Droylsden

The World Of Pure Imagination

My mind is expanded, my world is enchanted,
Listen out and you will hear
The churning of my factory near,
Maybe it's true, maybe it's far from,
But these golden tickets flash before you,
Forgery has been tried and less has it worked,
You might find yourself going berserk,
The imagination is what counts,
So make sure it's pure, or else
There is no cure...

Lili Jo Holt (11)
Fairfield High School For Girls, Droylsden

Napoleon's Army

Here is my army
Bold as brass
Here is my army
Standing on the grass
Here is my army
Ready for war
Here is my army
Ready for more
Here is my army
Brave and true
Here is my army
Coming with me to Waterloo.

Jessica Bridge (11)
Fairfield High School For Girls, Droylsden

More Than A Day

It's under the poppies, when he died, that he lay,
but my father, he fought, and deserves more than a day,
more than a pin that you wear on your clothes,
more than the songs your singers have chose.

For if not for him, don't you understand?
Not for my dad, you today would not stand.
You would be separated, unheard and lost in translation,
have no example of bravery worth celebration.

Why does he who died, for you, get a day?
When he gave his life, for you to be free today.
He should be remembered every day of every year!
So when his sacrifice is mentioned, let me hear you cheer!

As the soldiers who fought and battled to be free,
they were truly amazing, like the man who fathered me,
So please, I want him remembered,
so he knows, for his part,
that we're forever grateful, from the bottom of our hearts.

'Cause it's under the poppies, when they died, that they lay,
but the soldiers who fought deserve more than a day.
So *take* the freedom that they won for you,
as it came with great sacrifice, and you know it's true.

Rachel Madeline Thomas (13)
Kings Monkton School, Cardiff

Pineapple On Pizza

Every day there are people talking about me
Arguing who's wrong and who's right
I'm such a controversial topic
But at the end of the day...

I'm just a pineapple on a pizza
What's so wrong with that?
I just appeared on a tree one day
And people took me down

I travelled by boat on the sea
And by a truck on land
Soon I arrived at a factory
And got cut right up

Now I'm tiny little pieces
Scattered about
After that, I was loaded on a truck
Once again, I was off
On an adventure to become.

Pineapple on a pizza
Soon I arrived in a little corner shop
Had I finally made it?
No, not yet at least

When I arrived
Some people took the box I was in
And put me in the back

A day passed and...
Finally...
They picked me up
And sprinkled me on luscious tomato and cheese
But wait, what are they doing?
They were putting me in an oven!

I struggled to break free
But the cheese held me down
Knocking me down
I stopped struggling
And gave up...
But wait...
They're taking me out!
I'm alive, thank you, Pineapple Gods,
And that's where I am now
Just pineapple on a pizza.

Jacob Thomas Chaloner (12)
Kings Monkton School, Cardiff

Teachers And Children (Chalk And Cheese)

Children, very ungrateful, very vile and very naughty.
I'm lucky I am no longer a child since I am almost forty!

From mucky fights and eating in class,
Those stupid jokes and silly comments, what a farce.
No homework and no pen and every pupil's
empty pencil cases,
"Hey, you over there, you are going to trip over your laces!"

Ah, feet up in the staffroom, a cup of tea and
my custard creams.
It's break time now, "Please don't wake me up from this
beautiful dream!"

After break time, I'm sad, my heart skips a beat,
It's back to the blackboard and that same old seat.
I walk to the classroom with my head down, staring at the
wooden floor,
"Headmaster, control your children, they are literally
declaring war!"

When I start the lesson, I just want it to end,
A moment of silence, to me just lend.
"Colin, what's the capital of Australia?"
"I don't know! I'm afraid to say Miss, your teaching methods
are a complete failure."

But after school and on a Friday night,

The world is my oyster and my life becomes light.
Ah, two whole days without those horrible children or any
awful fight.

Younis Naseem (11)

Kings Monkton School, Cardiff

Through Their Eyes

Her yellow dress, I could spot it in the trees
Her brown hair swayed, as she stumbled through the leaves

I followed as she marched, the sun was going down
I was losing sight of the yellow dress,
Until she was nowhere to be found

I search for her on end, all hopes were lost
That forest seemed to get smaller
There must've been a path uncrossed

All I heard were the birds squeak
I then stepped on a twig; I heard a shriek...

I ran as fast as I could, the cries were getting worse
Could this be the day? The end of this curse?

The screams were deafening, I couldn't hear my own
thoughts
My eyes were full of tears, my heart was racing, it wouldn't
be caught

A glimpse of yellow I saw in the leaves
Lying, crying on a broken tree, I had fallen to my knees

There she was, thank the Lord
But she was still screaming, that ear-piercing roar

A branch had collapsed, hammering her leg to the ground
I leaned and grabbed the branch, silencing the sound

I picked her up, wrapping my arms around her
I never wanted to let her go; I wish I could've been sure...

Abi Thomas (12)
Kings Monkton School, Cardiff

Through Their Eyes Timeline

First-ever humans
Through their eyes,
They saw life for the first time,
And peace would come.

World War I
Through their eyes,
People fought over ruling other countries,
Misery and death and bravery.

World War II
Through their eyes,
Chaos and city and towns were destroyed,
We people are destroying our own planet.

Mahatma Gandhi
Through his eyes,
Everyone was equal to one another.

Malala Yousafzai
Through her eyes,
Girls have rights,
They have rights to good education.

Factory owners
Through their eyes,
They only care about money,
And they cannot see what is happening to global warming.

People who help Earth (by planting plants)
Through their eyes,
They can see what the future is going to become,
And that is... no future.

Me
Through their eyes,
I can see the world changing so rapidly,
We need to protect our planet,
Help the community,
Stop global warming,
Have equal rights,
Stop racism,
Stop wars,
And enjoy life in a better way.

Johnny Jiang (13)
Kings Monkton School, Cardiff

Attention

I step out, clutching my books,
hiding behind my coat.
I plug in my headphones
hoping to block out their thoughts and my own.
I never wanted the attention.

I know they're not looking, but I can still feel their eyes
burning.
Dodge the mirror, dodge the mirror, dodge the mirror.
The outfit I spent hours choosing doesn't look the same.
Not in front of the glass. The picture in my head crumbles.
My millions of voices snicker and sneer.
I never wanted the attention.

Throw the school bag down.
Change into comfort.
Change into something you can hide in.
They say they don't judge. They say it doesn't matter.
It's true, they don't. But I do.
I can't handle my own attention.

My parents don't understand, how could they?
I pour out my heart
and it falls onto the floor.
No one can help.
I want the attention to go away.

It wasn't my choice, it's in society's hands.

They drag me down.
Of course, I want to look great,
but I'm busy looking at the magazines.
The models are perfect, just perfect.
They want all the attention.

Sitara Christina Kaur Bhal (13)

Kings Monkton School, Cardiff

A Day In The Life Of An Ant

I wake up in my anthill, not really alone
like the queen up there on her throne,
hundreds of ants all scurry around.
Time for breakfast, some apple we found
in the human's picnic basket they left lying around.

We went out to the park but no time for play
I am an ant, we work hard all day.
Children playing, their feet we must dodge,
as we rush around gathering food to pay for our lodge.

Then the rain comes, for cover we run,
the children all go home, it's ended their fun.

Some cover we find in the branches of a huge blossom tree,
we huddle together in a hole in the bark
as the thunder clashes and the lightning sparks.

Then the rain stops and it's time to head home,
our troop moves as one, we are never alone.

Back at the anthill our bounty we eat,
before it's time to sleep,
ready for the next day when it begins again,
for I am an ant, there's no time for fun!

Chaya Young (12)
Kings Monkton School, Cardiff

I Have A Dream

The cold breeze on that day
The sun glistening and the crowd
The crowd roaring like starved lions
As I stepped on the podium
The roaring stopped
As though everyone in the crowd became mute
A sense of anticipation was flooded out by the unease
Even the sun wore a sense of sadness on his face
Throughout the first part of my speech
Looks of fear, unease, and denial flooded the atmosphere
During the second part, the atmosphere changed
As though the world started to smile again
The atmosphere overflowing with pleased people
The fragrance was extraordinary
Multiple people from multiple backgrounds
All together
All united
Everyone in the crowd coming for one thing
A multitude of people combined to
Make up the fragrance of the crowd
And when I stepped off the stage
A flurry of applause echoed throughout.

Sameer Jilani (12)
Kings Monkton School, Cardiff

The Big Bad Blitz

People running all around,
Bombs crashing all day long,
Planes soaring ready for war,
Hitler roaring his commands,

Everyone crying just like me,
I really haven't had much tea,
My husband's off to fight,
This really isn't right,

On the 2nd of December,
I do remember,
On that horrible night,
When it was still light,

The bombs came raining down
And the sky becomes brown,
The searchlights dancing through the sky,
Never knowing when to say bye,

While menacing Messerschmitts mingle in the lights,
Manoeuvring and dancing at dizzy heights,
The old men in the planes,
While firefighters fight in the flames,

When I get out I see,
My house in ruins all around me,
Children crying,
Mothers weeping,

That night was severe, there is no doubt,
We had a hard blow but they can't knock us out.

Oliver Morgan (11)
Kings Monkton School, Cardiff

I Just Want A Home

A few months ago, my mum was put down
I got a new home
It was amazing
Awesome, great, fantastic

They couldn't keep me for long
Around a week or two
Gone
That's been five homes I've been in before the age of one
I'm staying here for now
It's horrible
I feel scared
Frightened, nervous, afraid

Please get me out of this box
I can't breathe
Please help
They now kick me
Punch and hit

The shelter came and rescued me today
I've found my home
He's lovely
Smart, cool, fun

We've been on two walks already
Now our third
Third and final

In the field
Roses, lilies, poppies

This feels special
So, so special
But suddenly
He stops
Just stops
And drops...

Molly Williamson (12)
Kings Monkton School, Cardiff

I Love You

I lie in my bed and look at my feet,
My grandchildren sit at the side of me,
I kiss and I hug them, I listen and talk with them,
My own two children don't even care.

My head is full of thoughts sitting here,
Looking at the old people around me,
I think, *am I really this old?*
My grandchildren say no and we say goodbye.

In the morning, I'm not in bed,
I'm in a place full of fluffy clouds,
I look down on my children, one says,
"Why did I not say goodbye?"
The other says, "Why was he taken now?"

I look around my brand new home,
I will now see my dear wife again, it's been too long,
I will now feel her warm, wet kisses she used to give me,
I will now feel her gentle hugs.

I love you, my dearest wife.

Lucy Robinson (13)
Kings Monkton School, Cardiff

Only Dream

You all think you're unlucky if you don't get the new trend,
but what's the point if everything has to end?
I'm just a girl with nothing but a tent, I could only dream of
a house with bricks and cement.
I'm on my own in this empty land, I've got no one to hug or
hold my hand.
I can only imagine in my mind, what it would be like to leave
this lonely world behind.
You all take stuff for granted like TVs and cars, the best
thing I've got is the stars.
You watch TV and there's an advert of me, but you don't
care about what you see.
You see me on your pads and phones, but that doesn't
make you care for my cries and moans.
I'm a homeless girl, you don't care and you never will, I'm
the equivalent of rubbish on a landfill.
So when you go to bed tonight, remember me and hug me
tight.

Lily Thomasson (11)

Kings Monkton School, Cardiff

A Boy

I found out my friend
A boy had leukaemia
It would be ending soon
We all heard we would help
Sending letters to Liverpool
Gareth Bale, Ryan Gigs and the Welsh team
Each day we wrote
But my table got Gareth Bale
Day by day his mum came
In with different things
But today lots of beads
At times he went for leukaemia treatment
The beads went around the whole classroom
It's been about one-month now
Surprisingly the only team to respond
Were Liverpool
Liverpool found it touching.

They sent the whole class all their signatures
We set up an assembly for him
All his Liverpool gear
December now
The bell just rang to say
His leukaemia treatment is finished
And the leukaemia is gone!

Samson Paul John Reekie (11)
Kings Monkton School, Cardiff

How A Homeless Person Sees The World!

I live on the dirty and muddy streets.
Everyone else lives in a warm, cosy house.

I own horrible and torn up clothes.
Everyone else owns lovely and warm clothes.

I can't buy anything from the shops because I have no money.
Everyone else goes by with a huge flotilla of shopping bags.

I fish food out of the bins or go hungry.
Everyone else goes around carrying or eating mouth-watering food.

I have to suffer when it rains.
Everyone else has a roof over their heads.

I feel like a stupid and ignorant peasant.
Everyone else strolls around with smug looks on their faces like queens and kings.

Am I a disgusting alien or a human being?
That is your question.

Manel Soleman (11)
Kings Monkton School, Cardiff

War Rages On

Bang! War rages on
My husband is already gone
Running and screaming in the house
Only the dog is as quiet as a mouse
Now no one is safe
Not even our little one, Rafe

Someone knocks on our door
I think
We have always been poor
I can't imagine my husband sprawled on the floor
I sink down and start to cry
Maybe I should say goodbye

The knock gets louder
And louder and louder
Bullets tear through the wall
My husband hasn't heard my call

Finally, I get up
I say, "Goodbye, little pup."
I walk out of the door
My heart feels sore
All these men lying on the floor,
Bang! War rages on...

Findley Hookings (11)
Kings Monkton School, Cardiff

War Time

Every second, every minute of every hour
One of us dies or gets hurt.
We die or get hurt
When a trigger is pulled.

We get up, we run, we walk
We get scared, we get sad
And we save people's lives.
There will be blood on the
Ground over here and there.

We always lose soldiers
We never get to see them.
Every chance we get to
See them it could be
The last time.

All our memories will wash
Away sooner or later.
We feel everything until
Bang, you start to slowly
Lose touch of everything.

The moment we touch the ground,
The moment we leave we always
Lose something important behind.
Any moment we could die.

Jacquelyn Chua (11)
Kings Monkton School, Cardiff

My Pet, Moomin

Her tail is curly like a pink pig
Her fur is soft like a fluffy cloud
She eats as fast as the wind

She pulls as hard as a tough rope
Her face is cute like a little bow
Her bark is loud like a thunderstorm

When she's happy she jumps like a trampoline
When she is sad, she's like a bubbling baby
When she's angry she growls like a grumpy tiger

She walks like a happy cheetah
She smiles like a cute monkey
She always makes me feel happy

Sometimes she makes me laugh
Especially when she splashed in the bath
When she's scared, she is like a squirrel

You're amazing to the end
You will always be my best friend.

Eva Leana Crothers (12)
Kings Monkton School, Cardiff

Are We Not Human?

I see kids hiding behind whatever they can find,
Watching as everyone dear to their hearts being taken
away,
Our playground full of blood,
What about peace and comfort of life?
What about our human rights?
Were they all lies?
I sit in the corner and cry,
This isn't right,
Are we not human?

All our dreams were shattered in a blink of an eye,
Drops of rain glimmering from the sun's light,
Destroying our homes and our lives,
And I sit in a corner and cry,
This isn't right,
Are we not human?

Do you not hear us screaming?
Do you not see our tears?
You can see we are in pain,
But you still choose to turn away,
Are we not human?

Zoya Ahmed (13)
Kings Monkton School, Cardiff

The Tribe

The rhinos I looked after would often stay in packs,
Poachers came by leaving dead bodies in stacks.
The rhinos would eat, sleep and play,
Poachers came by every other day.

The rhinos' favourite food was corn,
Poachers would kill them for their horns.
Most of them dead, blood all around,
The lucky survivors not making a sound.

For them to stop, they wanted money, I had none,
Next thing I know I'm being pointed at with a gun.
They took my food, water and house,
Next thing you know our village had a drought.

Now the rhinos are dying anyway,
I hope the poachers don't come back another day.

Chris Jones (14)
Kings Monkton School, Cardiff

A New Earth

Every day is something new
New challenges to face
The way we see a view
It's like tying a shoelace.

We're destroying Mother Nature
Yet we choose not to help
We are slowly damaging our future
As places are starting to burn and melt.

Imagine a world of peace
Where our future is bright
A world full of ice and trees
And beautiful sights.

Tomorrow will be different
So let's start making a change
Let's show our confidence
And step out of this cage.

Let our actions start the conversations
To give the world a deserved chance
And allow future generations
To take a glance.

Michelle Tendai Mubayiwa (12)
Kings Monkton School, Cardiff

The Bird Of Flight

The sun has risen
The moon is down
The songs of birds twitter around.

I have awoken in my dark palace of twigs
Shining light shines bright in the air
As I come out my palace of twigs
It all goes eerie in the woods today.

You can hear the wind howling in despair
The birds disappeared and all is silent
I keep on walking on a thin branch
The wind blows in and it shakes.

The branches swooping left to right
Suddenly I slip
Suddenly I fall...
Do I hit the ground or do I fly...?

The cold dead leaves hit me and I feel dead
I look up and see the tree
But that is not all I see
I see the sky...

Blake Fry (11)
Kings Monkton School, Cardiff

Through The Eyes Of Cancer...

I'm fighting through the battles,
I'm struggling through life,
I'm starting to lose all hope,
I don't know if I can cope.
Thousands of deaths around the globe,
I just wish I could be back at home.

Memories of happiness,
Circling round my head,
Remembering old times,
Playing around,
Cherishing those moments,
Because they're about to end,
Now they're tears running down my cheeks.

I pray for the day,
The day I could be saved,
But it seems that I'm beginning to fade away,
The light in my soul is burning away,
My sad life has finally ended today.

Rachel Liu (11)
Kings Monkton School, Cardiff

The Leader

Led by power and money
Advised to do this and that
Ask any old person and they say they hate me

My life is in danger
I can't even leave my own house
I feel I'm trapped in my own consciousness
Everyone I know relies on me
And all I have to do is rule the country

What I say can affect everything
Speech after speech, they're all the same
I can't make a difference even though I'm leading

I long for freedom
I long to be free
But when there's a leader
Nobody's really free
Even I can't change that.

Morgan Joseph Bleasdale (12)
Kings Monkton School, Cardiff

The Fox

The fox set off on a quest
To find food but
He makes this his test
Children wait for food.

They all know Daddy's the best
The fox moves slowly to
Avoid being spotted
He runs so fast
He needs to take a rest.

A rabbit lay in plain sight
He said, "Be my guest."
The fox moves quickly
To the rabbit and then
Bam!

The rabbit disappeared
All of the children so hungry for food
Daddy fox comes home empty-handed.

Mother fox hangs him on a crest
Mother fox feeds the children
Foxtail soup.

Jaden Rohan (12)
Kings Monkton School, Cardiff

I Wonder When

You think it was insulting
Being told to 'brighten up' by teachers while they scowled at you
Being told to 'get some friends' by the people who made sure you had none
Being told that you 'failed' by people who pretended they expected anything more
I'm a joke – that people will never understand – but is told over and over
Every time it just gets a little bit harder
Every time they cut a little bit deeper
Every time the world becomes a little darker
And I wonder when they'll block out the sun completely.

Aron Hurt (13)
Kings Monkton School, Cardiff

The Blitz

The bombing in London is at its peak,
Lying in bed every night in fear that it would be our last,
So far we have been extremely lucky,
As both of our neighbours have been bombed more than
once.

"It's three in the morning," my mother cried,
"Do the Germans ever rest?"
We rushed to the bunker,
Where we could hear many screams,
By the time the raid was over it was six in the morning.

When we got out of the bunker,
Much to our despair,
Our house was all rubble,
I saw a single tear run down my mother's cheek.

Callum Morgan (11)
Kings Monkton School, Cardiff

Homophobia

The people of my community shunned me,
The people I live with shunned me,
The people I called my friends shunned me.

The family I grew up with shunned me,
They called me names: 'queer', 'homo', 'sinner'.
The more they said,
The more I pulled the knife closer to my throat.

The more I was spat on,
The more death loomed closer,
The more they fought,
The happier I became.

The more that stand up,
The more we care.
The more you support me,
Better the world becomes.

Beau Alexander Deabreu (14)
Kings Monkton School, Cardiff

A Whale's Song

A smudge on a painting of endless sea,
You can hear their songs from miles away,
Together they are where no one else may see.

Then like a fly to a spider's web,
A whale swam right into its trap,
The curtain is drawn, now the show is over.

A vast isolation but only a breath away,
Now at the point of no return,
They must now leave no matter how much they stay.

A feeling of anguish sets in,
The low hums still echo the deep waters of the whale lost at
sea.

Ellexa Kingdon Bevan (13)
Kings Monkton School, Cardiff

Benji

Hi, my name is Benji, my life is the worst
I used to be happy but now I am a war dog
Here is my story, I grew up healthy
With a lady and a boy who loved me so much
All the great times we had together
When the boy would throw me a green, small ball
One day we were going on a plane
I came on a spinning circle
They never came back for me
A day later a man in an army coat found me, I was scared
first
Next thing I knew I was fighting in the army...

Edward Huw Collingwood Lewis (11)
Kings Monkton School, Cardiff

Trapped

Everyone is staring
Her heart begins to sink
Thumping, pounding
Still, she can't think

Vision all blurred
Can't even breathe
Can't see clearly
Posture all weak

She must hide
Can never let anyone see
What feelings are, she says
Bottled up inside of me

She can't escape
Just wants to leave
Because it's not her
Trapped inside of me.

Priyal Dilip Rupalia (12)
Kings Monkton School, Cardiff

I Am...

I am real, I am living, I am breathing,
I feel pain.

I wander the same path,
I pass the same tree.
Carrying the same weight
And pain every day.

I mustn't stop walking, if I disobey
The whip will come crashing down on my flank.

Every day I hope that someone will come
And heal my pain and sorrow.
I am an animal with feelings,
I am a donkey with no rest.

Amelia Jeffries (12)
Kings Monkton School, Cardiff

Malala Yousafzai: 'One Child... Can Change The World'

She spoke out
Women refused an education
Not allowed
Banned.

She spoke out
And got shot in the eye
Wanted to escape
Freedom.

Malala spoke out
For better education
More opportunities for women
Change.

Jacob Mankoo-Pearson (13)
Kings Monkton School, Cardiff

Through My Eyes, A Female Football Player

When I was growing, I thought I was wrong,
No playing with dolls, I made myself strong,
Slept with a football instead of a bear,
I hated my hair, name and what I'd wear.

I played my first game when I was just five,
That Sunday on the pitch, I came alive.
There's nothing that compares to that feeling,
The thrill of the game, it feels like dreaming.

I played with boys, was better than the rest,
Being a girl in their eyes, second best.
My coaches always supportive and kind,
Other parents wanted me left behind.

As boys get older, the gender gap grows,
And then by high school, their envy would show.
They started to say such monstrous things,
"You freak, you're a lesbian!" they would sing.

"How can a girl play football? You're so bad!"
"My dad watches girls football, makes him mad."
They made me feel worthless, I didn't belong,
I still carried on training, growing strong.

"You think you're so good!" is what they'd say,
Practically bullying me every day.

They were jealous, you see, of a girl like me.
A skilled player, with the ball I was free.

I had a passion that grew deep inside,
I focused on that fire, so I never cried.
A victim? No way! I just wouldn't be!
I trained harder, for longer, true to me.

They still try their hardest to shoot me down,
When they do I pause and adjust my crown.
Now I'm on TV, three lions on my shirt,
It's only the tackles that bring the hurt.

Scarlett Sarah Smith (12)
Oulder Hill Community School, Rochdale

Life Of A Coffee Mug

A coffee mug, we have all seen them
The life of one is very boring
But it is also a life of pain
The warm drink of coffee my whole body
I get this terror of near-death every day
My owner does not even think of me

Unlike other objects, I do not want to be used
I have become the new favourite mug
That means I am used nine to five and five days a week
After the small amount of torture, I wished I would get
dropped

The life of coffee mugs is boring
You are picked out at 9:10am then burned on the inside
Then you watch a person touch a magic black thing
Then it somehow makes symbols appear, a hanging piece of
paper
It is interesting how they do this over and over again
I thought they were meaningless

One day I saw my human very happy over a piece of paper
That puzzles me, some paper is worth more?
You would think I would know what coffee was
No, my owner drinks one sip of coffee
And he goes from tired to awake in a minute
My theory on that is black magic

Again, I wish I was dropped
So all the pain I have will end
And my questions about my owner
And what coffee is will end too.

Aziz Ahmad (12)
Oulder Hill Community School, Rochdale

J K Rowling

I had already decided I was an author,
I was still a small child who was in bother.
Me and my little sister snuggled up in bed,
I told her my story no one else had read.

I'm not grown up, a young lady,
Although my future is still quite hazy.
Now it's New Year's day,
My mother in her bed she lay.
Who knew where this led,
My poor mother is now dead.
I thought monsters were supposed to be under your bed,
But instead, they're inside my head.

I had already decided I was gonna write,
Even though I had cried all night,
My story is now all complete,
It's nice and beautifully done and neat.

I sent it to a publisher far away,
A week later, it was rejected,
I didn't know what to say.
I tried and tried again,
Everyone said they left me in pain.

I didn't give up, not once or twice,
Until a man picked it up who was very nice.
Now everyone knows my name,

I'm full of joy and glorious fame.

I am now known as J K Rowling,
Do me a favour,
And listen to that voice inside of you howling.

Amber Saeed (11)
Oulder Hill Community School, Rochdale

Death Row Dad

The courtroom shut
And my sentence was announced,
I now have life
Behind prison cells!
I get no visits
And my family don't care.
My wife and two kids
Don't want to see me there.
They think I'm a killer
Of the President's brother,
I'm only a witness,
But listening to my explanation is a bother.
I would never hurt a soul,
I've never been that person!
So why are they blaming me?
This is really hurtful!
I've finally made my mind up,
Death row is my decision.
It'll make my time shorter
And get me out of this prison.
3rd of October is my last day,
My last meal will be amazing!
It's now in two weeks time
And I can't stop shaking,
I know I don't deserve this!
I am innocent, that's the truth,

I wish I could stay.
But now it's time to go,
I want to see my kids
And say my last goodbye,
But they're not coming,
Which always makes me cry.

Lewis Whiteside (12)
Oulder Hill Community School, Rochdale

Muhammad Ali

Everyone knew when I stepped into town
I was the greatest fighter around
A lot of people called me a clown
But I am the one who called the round
The people came to see a great fight
But all I did was put out the light
Never put your money against Cassias Clay
For you will never have a lucky day

"Ow, Clay swings with a right, what a beautiful swing!"
And the punch raises the bear clear out of the ring
Liston is still rising, and the ref wears a frown
For he can't start counting till Sonny comes down
Now Liston disappears from view
The crowd is getting frantic
But our radar stations have picked him up
He's somewhere over the Atlantic
Who would have thought when they came to fight?
They'd witness the launching of a human satellite
Yes, the crowd did not dream when they lay down their money
That they would see a total eclipse of Sonny
"I am the greatest!" Muhammad Ali.

Ethan Miller (11)
Oulder Hill Community School, Rochdale

Winston Churchill - Through Their Eyes

I was in my office when I heard a knock
On the door, beside the clock
I saw the man who walked right in
Very tall and very thin
And in his hand was a letter
Which couldn't have looked any better.

In the letter were some notes
My full body filled with hope.
I read the letter, it sounded very sinister
And at the bottom, said, 'Be the prime minister'
I jumped around, filled with joy
It was almost like I was a little boy
I had a rough time as a leader
It was like I was England's special feature
But I won the war
Without a sore
All from behind my office door
We got rid of the Holocaust
Although it was a big cost
It may have cost 416,000 men
But has saved the great Big Ben
We got rid of Hitler, made it to breaking news
And, of course, we saved the Jews.

Louie Norbury (12)
Oulder Hill Community School, Rochdale

Time Is Priceless

Every day she bothers me,
Every day she makes me food,
That I don't even like,
She treats me like a kid,
I wish she would just go,
I scream at her every day,
"I hate you,"
Today I asked her to leave the house,
She went in her car and drove off,
I was all alone at home, enjoying life
Midnight and no sign of my mum,
So I called her phone
Somebody else picked up
She asked me who this was,
I replied with
"I'm this person's phone's son"
She said she was a doctor
She said, stumbling with her words
"Your mother was in a car accident
The car rolled over six times,
She didn't make it."
I hung up the phone
I dropped to my knees
I looked up and whispered,
"I love you, mum!"

Andy Ho (12)
Oulder Hill Community School, Rochdale

Through Their Eyes: Footballer

The ball bounced off my head
Like it was about to take off
Fans chanted in my mind
To me, it was totally fine

Two minutes left to go
And it went out to be our throw
I wanted to score the final goal
But then the ref blew the final blow

A heavy boulder hit my back
Turns out it was a team pack
Jumping and shouting
I really should do more ranting

As more and more piled on
It ended up like a marathon
People running, laughing, shouting,
It turned out to be the full stadium chanting.

Teammates laughing, chanting, messing
Pouring beer all over the netting
Stewards didn't treat it as serious
At the end of the day, it was hilarious.

Esmé Grace Mills (12)
Oulder Hill Community School, Rochdale

Army Man

Running the ten miles was tough,
Every last breath needed a huff and a puff.
Crashing through the finish line, I knew
That I was not yet through,
To the next round where boxing was the game,
With each punch, I lived up to my nickname,
Josh the incredibly lame.
I struggled but I knew,
Joining the army was the main aim,
I knew how close I was and how an ounce more effort
Would lead me to fame
Picking up my hat was the proudest moment for me,
A moment which threw me back to remembering my family.
My family who served for our great country in WWII
Like I shall do for you,
I've always told myself I can,
Because I am the army man.

Josh Charlton (12)
Oulder Hill Community School, Rochdale

Never Give Up: Poem About J K Rowling

J K Rowling was unemployed
She was rejected fourteen times
No one came to her side
Still, she had resilience all the time

People don't enjoy reading her books
They say she completely sucks
I think it's not her luck
Unfortunately, they think her books are yuck

She said, "There's no point giving up."
J K Rowling thought about making a book
And she did, it was called Harry Potter
The next day, there was a call on the phone
A gentleman said, "Your Harry Potter book is on fire! You're hired!"
She was so happy
From that day she is very popular now
She now earns £65,000,000.

Khadija Ali
Oulder Hill Community School, Rochdale

Lua

They call me Lua,
Petite and spruced
Larger than life
I rule this roost.

My coat, a collection
Of perfect curls
Like glistening golden rings
My eyes are ebony beads,
Sparkling in the sun.

5am, time to get up,
Scratching the door,
Will I make them look?

Once breakfast's all gone,
It's outside for a bit,
Then it's back to the lounge
And there I sit.

As the front door shuts,
And everyone leaves
I jump down from the window
And begin my routine.

Scanning the ground for leftover food
Sniffing the floor for strewn about socks
The door unlocks...
It's Grandma!

Natalie Marshall (12)
Oulder Hill Community School, Rochdale

Imran Khan

As a boy I came from nothing
My only escape was the dream of playing cricket
"Just throw the ball hard and aim for the wicket."
I repeated over and over again
As this was my ticket to freedom

As I got a chance to play
Pride ran through my veins every day
I became a nations hero
The boy with nothing became his own superhero
I became victorious
As my fans thought me glorious

Success followed me everywhere
And I no longer felt despair
Rising to my biggest challenge
I became a national leader
My father taught me to always rise against the storm
Especially when it was my turn to perform.

Salman Alam (12)
Oulder Hill Community School, Rochdale

I Want To Go Home!

Home is where I want to go
Come rain, shine, sun or snow
Home is where I could be
With my mum eating tea
Home is where I should be
Not here picking cocoa beans
Today's the day I turn eleven
I've been here since I was seven
The men who took me seemed rather nice
But for tea, I get water and rice

Home is where I want to go
Come sun, rain, shine or snow
Home is where I should be
Not here picking cocoa beans
Today's the day I turn eleven
I've been here since I was seven
When I'm 'bad' they shoot their guns
I think I should be with my mum.

James Robinson (11)
Oulder Hill Community School, Rochdale

Jesy Nelson

It became too much, people
It got too bad
They were telling me to kill myself
But I hid my thoughts all inside me
They were telling me that I was the ugliest one
And I felt so alone and lonely

My phone was erupting with messages all negative
I thought I would have fitted in
But they were all wrong, telling me to get social media
I was flying with success
But wanted to go back to being normal
I felt different.

I would wake up and cry
I didn't accept my body
I would get called a cow
And I lost a lot of weight
I would care more about my looks
I was unhappy.

Brooke Cosby (11)
Oulder Hill Community School, Rochdale

Life Of A Platypus

As I came out of my hole,
I saw a furry little mole,
I tried to catch it,
But my run wouldn't match it.
I went for a swim,
As the sky went dim,
I came out very wet,
As the moon did set,
And as the sun rose,
I did my jump pose!
I went back to my hole
And still saw that same mole!
I ate some worms
That made my tummy churn,
I tried to wish it away,
But trying wasn't the way
I eventually lost it
So I didn't need to spend a cost
I went back outside,
To find another mole alongside,
I guess that's my life,
I hope it's not strife.

Millie Grace Finan (11)
Oulder Hill Community School, Rochdale

Through Their Eyes: BTS

"BTS! BTS! BTS!"
That's what I hear after every concert,
"BTS! BTS! BTS!"
That's what I think after every concert.

I am someone in a famous music group,
So busy we have concerts everywhere.
I am someone in a famous music group,
Where there is not enough time for family.

I have enough fans to cover Korea
Just because of my job.
I have enough fans to cover Korea,
Just because I'm famous.

I love all my fans
But I would like to be with my family if I could
I love all my fans
But I would do anything to be with my family.

Alina Jiang (12)
Oulder Hill Community School, Rochdale

Like Always

He logged on again
And there they were
Just like they always were
There, ready to write their horrible, mean messages
He was just waiting to see who would type first
It was normally Jack, fast at typing and very mean
But this time it was different
No one was typing
When suddenly Jacob added five new people to the group
At once they all started typing
All eight of them
The messages were
'you are so ugly'
'you should kill yourself'
'no one likes you'
He just sat there
Tears flowed down his cheek.

Samuel Bowers
Oulder Hill Community School, Rochdale

Through Their Eyes: Rosa Parks

I step onto a bus,
Without a slight bit of fuss,
And yet all eyes are on me,
A sprinkle of joy runs through me as I spot a seat,

Just a few moments pass by and on steps
An angelic and perfectly pure white woman,
She tells me to give her my seat,
My body fills with anger,

Who does she think she is?
The queen,

When she is just another human,
The only difference is our skin,
So I ignore,
As she asks me once more
The bus fills with gasps
And my body fills with pride,
I just stood up to racism.

Hanna Emilia Balcarek (13)
Oulder Hill Community School, Rochdale

The Last One

Stood there, looking up the town,
Stood there with a great big frown
Aeons and aeons, I have been stood here now
Cursed to never move
My roots are here
I let her pick an apple now they dont grow
Cursed by God, but no one will know

Couples carve into me, their initials and names
A great oak they say
A great oak I am they claim
Surrounded by a garden
Eden was its name
Fruit, flowers, veg galore
Then that snake came, and nothing grows anymore
Everything rotted and Im the last one

Hollie Nugent (12)
Oulder Hill Community School, Rochdale

Why?

My name is Wallie, I am a walrus,
I remember a bit ago when everything was good,
It's cold in the Arctic but my family was there,
I knew they would,
We had a great life,
My family and I,
And I had an amazing wife,
We swam and played and had lots of fun,
But as you know all good things come to an end,
When the humans came to the Arctic,
We were very confused, but we decided not to care,
So we decided to keep playing in the fresh air,
The next day, my family, my wife, were just not there...

Imogen Rose Evans (11)
Oulder Hill Community School, Rochdale

I Am A Turtle

Animals that deal with plastic
I am a turtle
Who lives in the sea
I like to swim
And I have a big family
But now I am lost because of plastic
I got tangled in it
And now my family left me.

I'm all alone, sad and upset
And also in a lot of pain
I can't see
Because a plastic bag is on me
I shouted 'help' but nobody heard
I had no hope

But then a human came
And helped me out and he saved me
Please don't use or throw plastic, it kills me.

Zakir Ali (12)
Oulder Hill Community School, Rochdale

Someone Help

The dark, gloomy nights by myself
Is the start of the pain
Tossing and turning on the rock-hard ground
Started to make my whole-body ache

Who am I?
All I do is beg
I dont know what to do anymore
All I can do is sleep
I cant survive much longer

Hopeless and desperate
Hiding in the shadows
Forgetting who I am

Please help me its not my fault
But no, I am thrown away
Hungry and horrified
What will happen to me?
Someone help.

Michael Charnley (11)
Oulder Hill Community School, Rochdale

Mohamed Salah: The Egyptian King

The Egyptian king and the king of hearts,
Scoring once the whistleblowing starts,
Doing his best and making the world stare
Wondering, *how perfect is that player with the afro hair,*
He moved from Roma to Liverpool
To the heart of every adult and child at school
Not once did we doubt his talent potential
And we always knew his presence in every game is essential
After every goal, he prayed to God and kneeled
And we prayed along that Mohammed Salah would never
leave the soccer field.

Abdul-Sami Shakeel

Oulder Hill Community School, Rochdale

Through Their Eyes: Dogs

Humans don't deserve us
When they come home, we're waiting
As soon as they walk through that door
They don't let us out in time and then moan
When we can't hold it any longer
And our humans will always be stronger
Some of us are allowed infinite treats
But some of us are left for dead
Some of us are extremely loved
But some of us suffer from severe neglect
So treasure us, we don't last forever
But while we're here, we will give you endless pleasure.

Aimee Lee Boileau (11)
Oulder Hill Community School, Rochdale

Penguins

The sun was in my eyes
And I could hear the baby penguin's cries
I got up and awoke
And give my friend Jimmy a poke
All around was melting ice
I wish my days were back to once

Diving in the ocean, we must be very careful
There could be a party of walruses and their bite can be
painful

The days pass by
And I just want to cry
As all my friends bring back less fish
All I have is one wish
Please take time
To look at the world through my eyes.

Meka Faith Reynolds (12)
Oulder Hill Community School, Rochdale

Refugee Poem

My life isn't the same
I used to live in Sudan
Where everything was right
I used to live in Sudan
Where I was happy and glad
My family lived in Sudan
Where everything was right
But now my heart has broken
Nothing will ever fix it
Not even the happiest of dreams
But finally, the day came
Where I would live in a house
Far away from Sudan
But at least I'm living in a house
And this house is where my heart is.

Samuel Stephen Shaw (12)
Oulder Hill Community School, Rochdale

Water Lizard?

I'm surrounded by white but see no light
The colour may seem bright, but all is night

One last push and I manage to open a crack
The top opens and I notice the hunger and food I lack

I tumble out the bowl like an object
Looking around however, I can't see what I suspect

Managing to get up and find myself surrounded by green,
yellow and blue.
My stomach rumbles and I say, "Yes I know, I'm hungry too."

Ikhlaas Goraya (12)
Oulder Hill Community School, Rochdale

Marilyn

Marilyn Monroe
That's my name
Circling attention, birds let's say
Immensely huge fame
Unfortunately, fame has a price to pay
Pain.
It was all good at first
No peace, it had gotten worse
Always expected to impress
Judged on the way I dress
Laugh
Talked
Walked
The weight of the world on me
Small little me.
I'm at peace now
Six feet under.

Marilyn Monroe
That's my name.

Chloe Chirozva
Oulder Hill Community School, Rochdale

Through The Eyes Of Jesy Nelson

When we finished 'The X Factor'
I had to get social media as it was a must
After a while, I got lost in a universe that felt unjust
On a daily basis flicking through
Comments made that just weren't true
Sometimes it was hard as some words were painful
And now I'm scarred with rejection
Because the words were hateful, and I'm told to remember
I must be mindful
To stay positive and eradicate the negative.

Gabrielle Sandra Owen-Davies (11)
Oulder Hill Community School, Rochdale

Bullying

Bullying,
I feel so alone,
I can't take it anymore,
I try to make myself look perfect,
It just doesn't work,

Every day I think, remember
About what happens to me
This is my last resort,
I just want to die.

I think it's kind of pathetic
The way we get judged for laughing,
Smiling or crying
No one deserves this
Not even me
Now please stop the nastiness
Before I leave.

Iman Ayub
Oulder Hill Community School, Rochdale

Adrift

As I drift in the sky,
I begin to cry,
My tears falling one by one,
Onto the moist land below.

Plants sprout from the soil,
As if they all woke up from a deep slumber,
My friend lightning strikes all the crops in sight,
Punishing them for waking up in my despair.

The plants wither away,
Lost in the soil,
The sun emerges with a morning greeting,
As I slowly begin to float away...

Joseph Oluwasola Ogunbo (12)
Oulder Hill Community School, Rochdale

Oulderhill Poem

Oulderhill first day finally comes,
Wake up in the morning freezing cold.
Eating breakfast, it's finally school,
Not school, high school.
The first day the sun's shining down
And the lights come in
Shining through the curtains
Putting the uniform on
Tying the buttons
Going out the front door
The sun goes out, it's freezing cold
Walking to school and finally get to school.

Hasan Amar

Oulder Hill Community School, Rochdale

Fake Friends Plus Real Friends

Friends are like sisters to you,
The ones that go are the ones that you don't need,
But the ones that stay are the ones that glow
Best friends have your back no matter
Whenever I am down or feeling unhappy
My friends are always there
Friends lighten your day
They're like sister souls
They're always here to help
But fake friends are ugly
So always treat people right.

Talbiya Khandaker
Oulder Hill Community School, Rochdale

The Hitman's Story

Being created to kill was against my will,
Having to kill someone for doing one mistake.
And yet their life I have to take.
All they did was tell a lie and yet they're left to die
From a gunshot to a silent death
All of them are dead, just like Macbeth
They could be rich and healthy
Or poor and full of insanity
But either way, I have to kill
Even though it's against my own will.

Austin Heneghan (11)
Oulder Hill Community School, Rochdale

Cyber Bullying: Jesy Nelson

They're just words
Tell that to the suicidal kids
Taking it every day, silent letters on screen
Never quite heard
Yet stings of 's***' ringing in my head.
Keyboard clicks
Swollen wrists
Tears roll down my cheeks
It displays
Displays the hate
They display towards me
My phone goes off
Another loss
I threw it all away
Ending my life.

Arooj Rafiq (12)
Oulder Hill Community School, Rochdale

David de Gea

I began my career with Athletico Madrid
I rose through the academy system, so I did
I must have brought the team good luck
Because we went on to win the UEFA cup

In 2011 I attracted the attention of Manchester United
And I was elected by Sir Matt Busby, player of the year
We have won many cups and shed many a tear
But my teammates will agree, we have nothing to fear.

Adam Garner
Oulder Hill Community School, Rochdale

In Their Eyes: A Neglected Life

Every day the same,
Every day nothing to eat,
Thousands of people, not one companion.

My knees bright red,
Bones cracking,
All the flesh jumping out of me,
I look like a pale piece of paper
That has red ink spilt all over it

Parents,
Carelessly they dump me in a box
Beaten with a thick wooden ruler on my thin wrist
Every day the same.

Adam Najeeb (12)
Oulder Hill Community School, Rochdale

FNAF VR Poem

I came to the door
Knocked, no one
The door slowly opened silently, creepily
I walked into the dining room, with the mindless bots
I stared down the dark creepy terrifying hallway
I took a seat, apparently super glue had spilled
And I couldn't get up
But they came, Foxy, Freddie, Chica and Bonnie
Now I've joined them, I am Glitchtrap.

Daniel Parry (12)
Oulder Hill Community School, Rochdale

Jesy Nelson Poem

Hello, my name is Jesy
My hair might be a bit messy
I love to sing all day long
I also like to write songs
I love to party with my gals
Coz they're all my lovely pals
Leigh-Anna, Perrie and Jade
They're all lovely girls
If you were to meet them, it sure would be a whirl
Work hard, follow your dreams
And you'll reach them.

Sophia Megan Ellison (12)
Oulder Hill Community School, Rochdale

Through Their Eyes: An Eagle

Flying so high in the sky
It's so easy to die
Wind racing by
So hard to stay high.

Polluted seas seem so foul
Memories start becoming much more beautiful
No fish to catch
No way to survive

So little trees
Little trees mean little food
Little food means little chance to survive
Chances of survival so, so low.

Ali Rehman (12)
Oulder Hill Community School, Rochdale

The Kitchen Chaos

Im a kitchen and Im a mess
Look at these cheeky children
They have no common sense
As they sit on the dining table
Waiting for their favourite food
They just cant stay stable
It's most certainly rude
They are munching on their fish and chips
Oh no, someone has farted
The chair is having an asthma attack.

Zara Hussain (12)
Oulder Hill Community School, Rochdale

The Humans

I am the king of the jungle
Yet you still steal from me and my pack
You still skin my fur and stuff me and seal me up in a glass
showcase
The humans use and seal us up like we're nothing, like we're
worth nothing
You may know me as the grumpy growler or the big dog
However, I usually go as lion, the scared, threatened,
dangerous lion.

Jennifer Rose Harrison (13)
Oulder Hill Community School, Rochdale

War Poem

'Twas a dark night in the ranches
All I could hear were branches
When we were marching
I was so very starving

Bang! Bang! Bang! Bang!
The opposing forces were here
Our men screaming for help
The others cleared the way

When I looked up
I saw men from hell
I sensed blood
And saw fallen men.

Ahmad Hussain (12)
Oulder Hill Community School, Rochdale

Dogs

We like to play around
I'm just a friendly hound
I just want to be loved
All I want is to be hugged

All of the other pets in the house
Get to catch a mouse
Because they're cats
They treat me like rats

All I wish for
Is more love
A new best friend
Who I can be with till the end.

Maryam Hussain (12)
Oulder Hill Community School, Rochdale

Poem About Jesy Nelson

It all started on X-Factor
Where I started a new chapter
Some people don't think
The words on the screen
Don't mean as much
So they have the right
To be mean
I would cry myself to sleep
Wishing it would stop
Maybe tomorrow it will cease
Then again, maybe not.

Imaan Faisal (12)
Oulder Hill Community School, Rochdale

Prison

As I sit here in my cell
And hear the guards yell
I am beginning to regret what I did
I am really starting to miss my kid

I hope he doesn't end up like me
Sat here sad and lonely
When I get out and start a fresh life
I'll do it all for my kid and wife.

Max Lees (11)
Oulder Hill Community School, Rochdale

Prisoner Of War

The air is as hot as the sun
Their war is nearly done
And yet we are still kept
We have not slept
Hot, hungry and scared.
It's as if they dared
To keep us longer still
We had to watch them kill
Just as a warning
As the sun was dawning.

Mia Lucy Wilson (13)
Oulder Hill Community School, Rochdale

Emergency Services

I'm a hero
To the people
And to me
I'm a zero
All I am
Is a normal person
Working for my family
I'm no superman
But a father
Of two beautiful children
And my salary is helping
The community.

Samuel Townson (11)
Oulder Hill Community School, Rochdale

Blue Cheese

I am stinky,
I have blue holes,
I never get bought
I'm left in the corner,
As days go by,
I grow stinkier and stinkier,
I rot more and more.
I hate cheddar cheese.

Aadam Sattar (11)
Oulder Hill Community School, Rochdale

Stronger

Trapped in my own home and forced to their will
Though I plead and though I thirst, their thirst may be to kill
Because I am a girl, they say is the reason
That by not signing over my royal rights, I commit treason.

All my pain would be over, they say
If I just gave in and let my brother be king
But what's the good in letting him win?
I am Mary the first, a mature woman
Yet he is more important than I?
Why has the whole of society gotten caught in the lie?

Perhaps it would be better if I just gave up
But my life isn't theirs, it's mine, society is corrupt
So if I can't take back what should be mine
I'll ensure my future is of my design.

My head held up high, I'll sign my rights away
I'll be kind and brave, no matter what they say
I will be a queen but not in the way I am supposed to be
Rising above all, the rest, being stronger, for me.

Abigail Louise Guppy (12)
St Philip Howard Catholic High School, Barnham

Nerd?

All about me
For some, it's a privilege
For others, it's a gift
Not everyone loves school
'Cause they think it's like a shift

My favourites are science, English and maths
And yes, indeed, I do try very hard
My IQ may be high
But I'm also very shy

I love to study, learn new things
It takes a while
And a lot of effort
But I do it with a smile

For some, it's a privilege
For other's a gift
Tests may scare me and you
But then afterwards
You can have fun like you always do.

Isabella Cyrulik (12)
St Philip Howard Catholic High School, Barnham

My Bedroom At Night

I sit alone in my deep, dark room
With only the shadows as my friend

I lie there in the dark
Creak, creak
I jump out of my bed in terror
I creep over to my door and peek outside
I breathe a sigh of relief
It is just my brother on the stairs

So I go back to my lonely bed
And then I hear a, "Hello..."
And it came from under my bed
Petrified, I slowly look
But it is just my new talking action figure
I take it and put it beside my lamp

I look around and see a person in the corner
Sitting, staring at me
I go closer to the person
But it's just my big teddy bear
I lie down
I am so tired
Still terrified, my eyes close
And I fall asleep.

Sophie Ryder
Uddingston Grammar School, Uddingston

Powerful Every Other Day

Every day I walk through the hall,
Apprehensive when the hands meet three
And I have to go home to the place I call prison.

My life there is misery, my very existence hated.
That's why I look forward to the morning when at nine o'clock
When I am able to go back to the strong person
Who is so different from the silent and weak person I am at home.

At school, I can be the person who is feared by everyone
At least I'm not the person who has to fear,
Like the person I've been my whole life...

There I can pick on the weak,
There I am the one who is avoided and obeyed.
People fear me here.
I am not the outcast, unlike the people I make my victims.

I don't know why I hurt him, I don't know why I make him feel this way,
Maybe it's because it makes me feel powerful
Unlike how I am every other day.
I don't know how it makes him feel.
Maybe the horrible, rude comments I say
Bounce around his head staying there
Forever torturing his very insides or...

If they fly over his head not bothering him in any way,
Like everything seems to.

I always wonder why I say these things,
Obnoxious words seem to slip off my tongue
Like sour milk leaving a terrible taste behind.

I used to think he deserves it - he can't read,
Can hardly count to twenty and can hardly control his arms,
But now I find that so hard to believe.
Maybe he is trying but the words he means to say get stuck,
Like how it is for me at home.

Millie Caplan Johnston (11)
Wallace High School, Stirling

October 31st

It was supposed to be a happy day.
It was supposed to be full of balloons -
glittery balloons, big balloons, blue balloons.
It was supposed to be full of presents -
big presents, sparkly presents
with my favourite song playing in the background
and on the table a cake, a rainbow cake which looked so
delicious.
I was ready to go over and eat my cake until
on the telly, the news began about Brexit being on the 31st
of October.
My birthday. Today.
I couldn't believe it, everything just seemed to go dull,
everything went dark.
I felt so many emotions: mad, upset, angry, annoyed.
I just didn't want Brexit to be on my birthday
because now, on the telly, I am going to start hearing
so many people just moaning about Brexit.
I mean, who cares about Brexit?

Anyway, later on that day, I was still watching the news,
honestly, I don't even know why.
I changed the channel and it was *still* Brexit
so I changed it again, again, again and again
and every single channel was Brexit.
Why, just why?
I hate Brexit.

At night I decided to go out trick or treating
to try and get my mind off Brexit.
So the time is about 19:00, I went to lots of houses
and got lots of sweets but every single house had Brexit on
their telly.
I could not take it anymore.
At about 21:00 I went home and tried to forget about Brexit.

Hannah Stretch
Wallace High School, Stirling

The Crow

My favourite bird isn't some majestic, exotic parrot,
Mine is the blackbird who is associated with death.
The black and dark purple feathers of fear,
Speed that could snap any human-like a twig when shards
of spine fly,
The black beak that devours souls,
The claws that snatch the life essence from your grip,
And a black, blank stare that shows no remorse, no fear.
The mystery that follows them could drive any man crazy,
And haunts us.
Murder of crows, murder of crows, crows of murder.

Keigan Thomas McLaren Robertson (13)
Wallace High School, Stirling

The Moon

On dark nights like this one,
I watch over the Earth,
Making sure that every night is peaceful and as it should be.

The trees whistle in the wind,
The shadows of mountains loom over villages,
The lights flickering s the day draws to an end.

I make sure the oceans are calm,
That the winds are fulfilled with everything they need.

I move from place to place,
Leaving once space behind as I travel onwards.

My job is never-ending;
I'm always travelling, always watching,
Always wandering.

Chloe Isabella Barwick (11)
Woking High School, Horsell

Paintbrush

The strands on my head,
Arranged in a beautiful collection of fine hair-like fibres,
Point undeviating towards the sky,
A destination that is an endless pathway of possibilities,
Patient yet eager to create something unique,
A portrait with a beautiful physique,
Or the most awe-inspiring painting you have ever seen.

Being picked out by the crowd is the most perfect gift,
One that you certainly don't want to miss,
Knowing that you are in the hands of a diverse artist,
Escaping into the world of beautiful signs,
Being able to twist things that most people see as straight lines,
Is only something I can do,
Something that I will always be able to do.

I can be submerged into many different colours,
But all the colours that have the potential to tell a story
Are the colours that make the artist shine with glory.

When I look above my paper,
I can see
The glorious smile glued to my artist's face,
A smile that I have been able to create,
A smile that I will always remember,
No matter how many times I get picked up and put back down,

This poem may have come to an end,
But my imagination, my drive to be the best
My ambition, my dedication,
Will never suspend.

Jessica Chan (13)
Woking High School, Horsell

War Camera

A cold shiver wrapped around me,
My fatigued cogs slowly clanked around
As my eyes blinked in moments.

This memory can now never be erased.
This memory will stay forever
In the small memory I have.
My cogs go rusty and start turning quicker.
I just stare.

Glass shatters everywhere as I realise
I have nothing left to give.
Flash.

My cogs slow down
As I blink once more,
Printing out the last thing
I will remember,
War,
Death.

Amy Rolfe (13)
Woking High School, Horsell

YoungWriters® — Est. 1991 —

YOUNG WRITERS INFORMATION

We hope you have enjoyed reading this book – and that you will continue to in the coming years.

If you're a young writer who enjoys reading and creative writing, or the parent of an enthusiastic poet or story writer, do visit our website **www.youngwriters.co.uk**. Here you will find free competitions, workshops and games, as well as recommended reads, a poetry glossary and our blog. There's lots to keep budding writers motivated to write!

If you would like to order further copies of this book, or any of our other titles, then please give us a call or order via your online account.

Young Writers
Remus House
Coltsfoot Drive
Peterborough
PE2 9BF
(01733) 890066
info@youngwriters.co.uk

Join in the conversation!
Tips, news, giveaways and much more!

 YoungWritersUK    @YoungWritersCW